LUDVEN

TRIO

for Piano, Violin and Violoncello
B♭ major / B-Dur / Si♭ majeur
Op. 97
"Archduke"
„Erzherzog-Trio"

Ernst Eulenburg Ltd
London · Mainz · Madrid · New York · Paris · Tokyo · Toronto · Zürich

CONTENTS

Ernst Eulenburg Ltd
48 Great Marlborough Street
London W1F 7BB

PREFACE

Beethoven composed his longest and finest piano trio between 3 March and 26 March 1811; he had made sketches for it the previous year at about the time he was working on the F minor String Quartet Op. 95. Almost at once he offered the piano trio to Breitkopf and Härtel (letter of 12 April), but it is clear from another and much later letter to the same firm (19 July 1816) that they refused the work because they thought the price too high. Beethoven seems then to have put publication out of his mind while he composed his last violin sonata (Op. 96) and the Symphonies Nos. 7 and 8 (1811-12). Then came the years when he was too distressed by personal problems to compose anything of real importance, and for some time he did not even try to get the works mentioned above either performed or published. At last, on 11 April 1814, the piano trio received what is thought to have been its first public performance, with Schuppanzigh (violin), Linke (cello), and Beethoven himself playing the piano. Moscheles was present, and thought Beethoven's playing lacked clarity and precision, though he recognized traces of the grand style. Spohr, who heard one of the rehearsals, was less complimentary; the composer's deafness had led to his banging the keys unmercifully in the loud passages, and depressing them so gently in the soft ones that there was no sound at all. Beethoven probably realised he had not done justice to his music for, apart from accompanying some songs, he never again played in public.

In 1815 he suddenly became active in getting all this splendid music published, and by the following year it was all on sale. Beethoven sold the piano trio both to S. A. Steiner of Vienna and to Robert Birchall of London; Birchall was to have only the British rights, and Beethoven asked him to allow Steiner's edition to come out first. This appeared at the end of September 1816, and Birchall's followed at the beginning of December. (A large number of the letters Beethoven wrote about getting this trio published have survived.)

Beethoven dedicated the trio to his most constant patron, the Archduke Rudolph, son of the Austrian Emperor. He was an excellent pianist, and no doubt he played the piano part himself from the set of parts that were specially made for him before publication. Beethoven also dedicated to him his fourth and fifth piano concertos, the Op. 96 violin sonata, two of the late piano sonatas, the *Große Fuge* for string quartet, and the great *Mass in D*. It is not clear why, alone of all these works, the piano trio should be known in Britain and America as the 'Archduke'.

In 1845, to celebrate the unveiling of the Beethoven Monument in Bonn, the theme of the slow movement was made into a hymn with words by Goethe ("Wer darf ihn nennen"). This version was later orchestrated by Liszt as an introduction to his cantata for the Beethoven centenary celebrations in 1870.

Roger Fiske

VORWORT

Beethoven komponierte sein längstes und hervorragendstes Klaviertrio vom 3. bis zum 26. März 1811. Seine Skizzen zu diesem Werk stammen aus dem Jahr zuvor, ungefähr aus der Zeit, in der er am Streichquartett in F-Moll, Op. 95, gearbeitet hat. Er bot das Klaviertrio Breitkopf und Härtel fast unmittelbar nach der Vollendung an (Brief vom 12. April), aber aus einem viel späteren Brief an den Verlag (19. Juli 1816) geht deutlich hervor, dass das Werk zurückgewiesen wurde, weil der Preis den Verlegern zu hoch erschien. Beethoven muss dann, als er seine letzte Violinsonate Op. 96 und die 7. und 8. Sinfonie komponierte (1811-12), den Gedanken an eine Drucklegung aufgegeben haben. Danach folgten Jahre, in denen ihn Sorgen und persönliche Probleme daran hinderten, etwas wirklich Bedeutendes zu komponieren, und so machte er gewisse Zeit gar keinen Versuch, die obengenannten Werke zur Aufführung oder Veröffentlichung zu bringen. Endlich, am 11. April 1814, fand vermutlich die Erstaufführung des Klaviertrios, mit Schuppanzigh (Geige), Linke (Cello) und Beethoven selbst am Klavier, statt. Moscheles wohnte ihr bei und meinte, es mangelte Beethovens Spiel an Klarheit und Genauigkeit, obwohl er noch Spuren des großartigen Stils erkennen konnte. Spohr, der eine der Proben gehört hatte, äußerte sich weniger schmeichelhaft; die Taubheit des Komponisten hatte dazu geführt, dass er in den lauten Passagen mitleidslos auf die Tasten einschlug und sie in den leisen so sanft herunterdrückte, dass sie überhaupt keinen Ton hervorbrachten. Vielleicht hat Beethoven dabei erkannt, dass er seiner Musik nicht gerecht werden konnte, denn, abgesehen als Begleiter einiger Lieder, hat er danach nie mehr öffentlich gespielt.

1815 begann er plötzlich, sich um die Veröffentlichung dieser ganzen herrlichen Musik zu kümmern, und schon im folgenden Jahr war alles im Handel. Beethoven verkaufte das Klaviertrio sowohl an S.A. Steiner in Wien, wie auch an Robert Birchall in London; Birchall sollte nur die Rechte für Großbritannien erwerben und Beethoven bat ihn, Steiners Ausgabe zuerst erscheinen zu lassen. Sie erschien Ende September 1816, und Birchalls folgte Anfang Dezember. (Eine große Anzahl von Beethovens Briefen, in denen er sich um die Drucklegung dieses Trios bemühte, sind bis heute erhalten.)

Beethoven widmete das Trio seinem treusten Gönner, dem Erzherzog Rudolph, Sohn des österreichischen Kaisers. Er war ein ausgezeichneter Pianist und er hat zweifellos selbst die Klavierstimme aus den Stimmen gespielt, die speziell für ihn vor der Drucklegung angefertigt wurden. Beethoven widmete ihm ferner sein 4. und 5. Klavierkonzert, die Violinsonate Op. 96, zwei der späten Klaviersonaten, die *Große Fuge* für Streichquartett und die große *Messe in D-Dur*. Unklar ist, weshalb in England und Amerika unter allen diesen Werken allein das Klaviertrio als „Archduke" (Erzherzog) bekannt ist.

1845, anlässlich der feierlichen Enthüllung des Beethovendenkmals in Bonn, wurde das Thema des langsamen Satzes für eine Hymne mit Worten von Goethe („Wer darf ihn nennen") verwandt. Diese Fassung wurde später von Liszt orchestriert und diente dann als Einleitung zu seiner Kantate für die Beethoven-Hundertjahrfeier (1870).

Übersetzung: Stefan de Haan

TRIO

Ludwig van Beethoven
(1770–1827)
Op. 97

I

Allegro moderato.

4

E.E. 1179

6

8

Scherzo. Allegro.

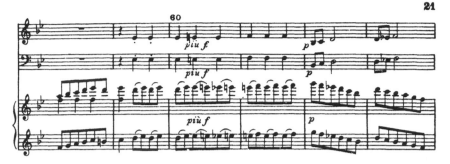

150

160

170

una volta la repetizione dal ✠ p. 19.
Fin al ✠ e la Coda

Coda.

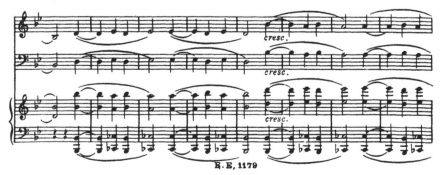

III

Andante cantabile ma pero con moto.

34

E.E. 1179

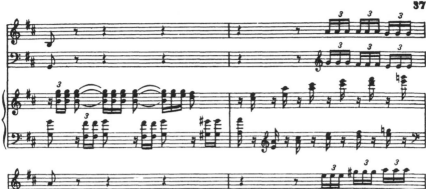

Poco più adagio.

120

cresc.

cresc.

cresc.

p

p

p

E.E. 1179

IV

Allegro moderato.

E.E. 1179

Presto.

260

270

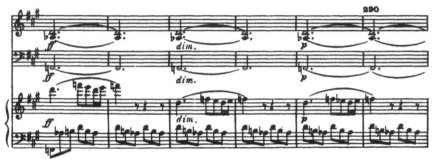